FURTHER
FOURTH
ASSESSMENT PAPERS IN

ENGLISH

ANSWER BOOK

JM BOND

Nelson

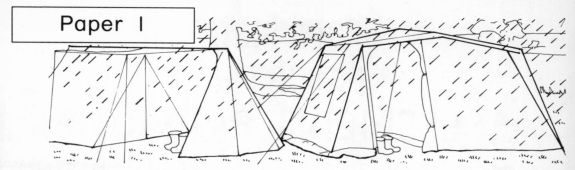

Read the following carefully and then answer the questions.
Where several possible answers are given, underline the correct answer.

All day it has rained, and we on the edge of the moors
Have sprawled in our bell-tents, moody and dull as boors,
Groundsheets and blankets spread on the muddy ground
And from the first grey wakening we have found
No refuge from the skirmishing fine rain
And the wind that made the canvas heave and flap
And the taut wet guy-ropes ravel out and snap.
All day the rain has glided, wave and mist and dream,
Drenching the gorse and heather, a gossamer stream
too light to stir the acorns that suddenly
Snatched from their cups by the wild south-westerly
Pattered against the tent and our upturned dreaming faces.

"All day it has rained" by Alun Lewis

1   The people in the poem were (at school, <u>camping</u>, picnicking, in a boat).

2   Was the weather fine in the early morning? (Yes, <u>no,</u> I do not know)

3   The poet described them as (<u>lying down</u>, sitting up, walking, fighting, putting up tents).

4   In the poem another word is used for **tight.** What is it?   taut

5   Why were the ropes taut? (They were tied too tightly, <u>wet weather always tightens ropes</u>, so the tent would stay up)

6   What was the weather like? (There was torrential rain, <u>it had rained steadily all day</u>, it was showery).

7   What kind of land were they on? (A garden, a field, a river bank, <u>common land</u>)

8   Our **dreaming faces** means (we had just awakened, <u>we were wishing the weather would improve</u>, we were lying down trying to sleep).

Here are some words and, on the right, a list of their meanings. Write the correct number in the space.

9 **conflagration** ....(3)....   (1) secret

10 **conservation** ....(6)....   (2) assembly

11 **constellation** ....(4)....   (3) disastrous fire

12 **conversation** ....(7)....   (4) group of stars

13 **confidential** ....(1)....   (5) one after the other, in order

14 **consecutive** ....(5)....   (6) preservation

15 **congregation** ....(2)....   (7) informal discussion

Complete the following:

16 **where** is to **place** as **when** is to .... time ....

17 **orange** is to **peel** as **egg** is to .... shell ....

18 **pages** are to **book** as **petals** are to .... flower ....

19 **car** is to **driver** as **bicycle** is to .... cyclist/rider ....

20 **walk** is to **run** as **speak** is to .... shout ....

21 **black** is to **white** as **host** is to .... guest ....

One word has a different meaning from the other words on the line. Underline that word.

22	demolish	damage	spoil	<u>defect</u>	smash
23	think	consider	ponder	contemplate	<u>reveal</u>
24	immaculate	<u>clear</u>	spotless	unblemished	clean
25	assemble	gather	<u>scatter</u>	collect	harvest
26	<u>valley</u>	summit	top	peak	tor

The following words end in either **ent** or **ant**. Add the correct ending to each word.

27 eleg<u>ant</u>   28 prud<u>ent</u>   29 adjac<u>ent</u>

30 abund<u>ant</u>   31 arrog<u>ant</u>   32 extravag<u>ant</u>

33 contin<u>ent</u>   34 immigr<u>ant</u>   35 cem<u>ent</u>

Match the following expressions with their meanings. Write the number in the space.

36 to call a spade a spade ...(7)...   (1) to begin to understand
37 to bury the hatchet ...(4)...   (2) back to work
38 by hook or by crook ...(8)...   (3) not to take sides – to remain neutral
39 a bolt from the blue ...(9)...   (4) to forget past quarrels
40 to sit on the fence ...(3)...   (5) neat and tidy
41 back in harness ...(2)...   (6) to change for the better
42 spick and span ...(5)...   (7) to be very outspoken
43 to turn over a new leaf ...(6)...   (8) determined to do something
44 to see daylight ...(1)...   (9) something unexpected

In the space, write the number of the adverb which best suits the verb.

45 **spent** ...(5)...   (1) brilliantly
46 **ate** ...(7)...   (2) attentively
47 **shone** ...(1)...   (3) bravely
48 **remembered** ...(6)...   (4) neatly
49 **listened** ...(2)...   (5) recklessly
50 **wrote** ...(4)...   (6) vaguely
51 **fought** ...(3)...   (7) greedily

Underline the correct word in the brackets:

52 Has Keith or Kim the (good, better, best) bat?
53 Of all the children he was the (late, later, latest) to arrive.
54 The more sweets you eat the (bad, worse, worst) your teeth will be.
55 I got the (few, fewer, fewest) mistakes in the class.

Below are some verbs which describe the noises made by water, feet, clocks, engines and wind. Can you sort them out?

strike	howl	drip	sigh	tick	shuffle	purr	blow
tramp	gurgle	throb	stamp	chime	pour	chug	

water		feet		clocks		engines		wind	
72 drip		73 shuffle		74 strike		75 purr		76 howl	
77 gurgle		78 tramp		79 tick		80 throb		81 sigh	
82 pour		83 stamp		84 chime		85 chug		86 blow	

87–93 Underline any of the words below which should start with a capital letter.

envelope   england   egyptian   film   fred   february

food   function   date   denmark   nation

month   august   manchester

94–100 Underline the words which are of common gender (can be either male or female).

actress   athlete   student   widow   policeman

friend   dustman   typist   girl   bride

bachelor   knitter   mother   child   cat

Paper 2

Complete each expression with a preposition.

Example: **off** the cuff

1 ...for... the most part   2 ...in... the long run

3 ...on... all fours   4 ...on... the other hand

5 ...for... better or worse   6 ...at... his wits' end

7 ...by... all means   8 ...up... to the hilt

From each of the words on the left make an adjective to fit the sentence:

9 **anxiety** The anxious woman waited for his return.

10 **peril** The mountaineers set out on their perilous climb.

11 **region** They heard the report on the regional news.

12 **choir** The choral society performed at the concert.

13 **method** They tackled the task in a very methodical way.

14 **length** Her long dress was much admired.

15 **ornament** The ornamental gate was painted white.

16 **metal** It made a metallic noise when it fell to the ground.

Underline the word which means the opposite of the word on the left:

17	**certain**	accept	careful	doubtful	sure	refuse
18	**humid**	dry	human	damp	wet	humane
19	**monotony**	monologue	variety	movement	motive	value
20	**numerous**	many	figures	number	small	sparse
21	**natural**	habit	eternal	adequate	artificial	permanent
22	**disperse**	scatter	cut	collect	plentiful	empty
23	**generous**	gift	thoughtful	money	intend	mean

7

Read the following carefully, and then answer the questions. Where several possible answers are given, underline the correct answer.

Nothing was before her but the grey sea and the sky, and the long, soft-roaring line of the surf. Through the sandals her feet could feel the hard, rippled pattern left on the sand by the waves.

Flocks of roosting gulls rose lazily as she reached the smooth, wet sand nearer the sea. Round any tide-left heap of seaweed, thousands of sandhoppers busily leapt, a strange, flurrying mist of movement in all the stillness. The record of other flurrying was written already on the hard sand: gouges and claw-marks and empty broken shells, where hungry herring gulls at dawn had seized any mollusc a fraction too slow at burrowing out of reach. Here and there an enormous jellyfish lay stranded, with great slashes torn out of the translucent flesh by the seagulls' greedy beaks. Out over the sea the birds coasted, peaceful, quiet.

from *Silver on the Tree* by S. Cooper

24 **Sandhoppers** are (birds, <u>insects</u>, people playing on the beach).

25 The **record of other flurrying** is (bird music, people playing on the sand, <u>signs on the sand</u>).

26 Which creatures were doing much damage? (Sandpipers, <u>herring gulls</u>, jellyfish)

27 To **roost** is to (<u>rest</u>, get hot, rise, leap).

28 To **coast** is to (fly inland, lie on the beach, <u>glide</u>).

29 **Tide-left** objects were (<u>things the tide had washed in and left</u>, things the tide didn't want, seaweed left in piles).

30 The molluscs avoided capture by (running away, <u>digging holes</u>, swimming out to sea).

31 **Translucent** means (<u>transparent</u>, transcendant, transient, transitory).

32–35 Which creatures are named in the passage?
gulls, sandhoppers, molluscs, jellyfish

36 Which plants are named? seaweed

8

Insert the correct letters in the spaces provided.

37 They had a barb _ecu_ e in the garden.

38 Pat wore her bi _kin_ i on the beach.

39 At night they snuggled down under their du _vet._

40 The wind was cold so they wore their ano _rak_ s.

41 They saw a vi _deo_ film of their Sports Day.

42 They went to the shopping pre _cinct._

Write one word in each space to complete the following expressions.

43 kith and _kin_   44 flesh and _blood_

45 beck and _call_   46 tooth and _nail_

47 thick and _thin_   48 hole and _corner_

49 ways and _means_   50 pick and _choose_

51 black and _white/blue_   52 hammer and _tongs_

Underline the word which is the same part of speech as the word on the left.

53	**laughed**	loudly	long	<u>ran</u>	wild	joke
54	**book**	read	<u>paper</u>	he	wrote	her
55	**tiny**	bee	wasp	flew	away	<u>large</u>
56	**sang**	<u>cried</u>	loudly	noise	scream	quiet
57	**loudly**	<u>quickly</u>	loud	quick	game	film
58	**they**	boys	children	<u>she</u>	teacher	class

Write a word, beginning with **a**, which has the same meaning as the word on the left.

59 stick   ad _here_   60 quicken   ac _celerate_

61 leave   ab _andon_   62 sharp   ac _ute_

63 change   al _ter_   64 plentiful   ab _undant_

65 shorten   ab _breviate_   66 try   at _tempt_

Punctuate the following by using inverted commas, question marks and apostrophes:

67–71 "What about the horse?" said Thorin. "You don't mention sending that back."

Underline the correct word to complete the following.

72 A person in charge of a museum is the (librarian, <u>curator</u>, minister, monk).

73 The most important player in an orchestra is the (conductor, violinist, trumpeter, <u>leader</u>).

74 A person who paints and papers rooms is a (<u>decorator</u>, mason, mechanic, paperback, paper-maker).

75 A person who performs operations is a (doctor, anaesthetist, <u>surgeon</u>, operator).

76 A person who goes where he is not allowed in order to steal game and fish is a (thief, trespasser, gamekeeper, <u>poacher</u>).

77 A person who repairs high buildings is a (stevedore, aviator, slater, <u>steeplejack</u>).

Add the suffix **-ing** to each of the following words.
Be careful! You may have to alter some of the words first, leaving out or doubling letters.

78	**put**	putting	**79**	**talk**	talking	**80**	**do**	doing
81	**swim**	swimming	**82**	**use**	using	**83**	**hide**	hiding
84	**hope**	hoping	**85**	**get**	getting	**86**	**carry**	carrying

87–93 Match the meanings with the words on the left.
Put the correct number in each space:

intimidate	3	(1) hermit
sedentary	6	(2) moisture
sediment	5	(3) frighten
humidity	2	(4) nearby
adversary	7	(5) dregs
recluse	1	(6) sitting
adjacent	4	(7) enemy

56 The (little, less, <u>least</u>) you can expect is to receive a letter.

57-58 The (hard, <u>harder</u>, hardest) you work the (clever, <u>cleverer</u>, cleverest) you will be.

Father stood on the crunchy snow on the terrace, sheltering in an angle by a window. He shivered a little, because his old suit really had worn very thin, but no one would notice him in this shadowy corner. He had taken no part in the festivities. In the ballroom he had been pushed aside by Arethusa and Araminta, who were ashamed of the shabby figure he cut. At the supper table the Stepmother had grabbed the best dishes that were presented to them and emptied his glass of wine as well as her own.

From *The Glass Slipper* by E. Nesbitt

59-63 Underline the statements that are correct:

<u>It was freezing</u>

The snow was melting
Father was very thin
<u>Arethusa and Araminta were ashamed of their father</u>

Father cut out shapes in the ballroom
His daughters thought his hobby was silly
The Stepmother spilt father's wine
<u>The Stepmother drank father's wine</u>

The Stepmother received a presentation
<u>The Stepmother was greedy</u>

<u>Father's suit was threadbare</u>

Father enjoyed dancing

Can you write the following abbreviations in full?

Example: **NE** North east

64	**PLC**	Public Limited Company	65	**Dept.**	Department
66	**PTO**	Please turn over	67	**USA**	United States of America
68	**MP**	Member of Parliament	69	**mg**	milligram
70	**DSS**	Department of Social Security	71	**BST**	British Summer Time

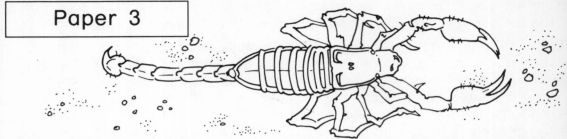

Paper 3

Read the following carefully, and then answer the questions. Where several possible answers are given, underline the correct answer.

The shyest and most self-effacing of the wall community were the most dangerous; you hardly ever saw one unless you looked for it, and yet there must have been several hundred living in the cracks of the wall. Slide a knife blade carefully under a piece of the loose plaster and lever it gently away from the brick, and there, crouching beneath it, would be a little black scorpion an inch long, looking as though he were made out of polished chocolate. They were weird looking things, with their flattened, oval bodies, their neat, crooked legs, the enormous crab-like claws, bulbous and neatly jointed as armour, and the tail like a string of brown beads ending in a sting like a rose-thorn. The scorpion would lie there quietly as you examined him, only raising his tail in an almost apologetic gesture of warning if you breathed too hard on him. If you kept him in the sun too long he would simply turn his back on you and walk away, and then slide slowly but firmly under another section of plaster. ...

From *My Family and other Animals* by Gerald Durrell

1 Where did he find the scorpion? (On top of the wall, under the plaster, in the community)

2 Its tail is likened to: (chocolate drops, brown beads, armour).

3 Self-effacing is (wanting the best for yourself, trying to be inconspicuous, appearing two-faced).

4-5 The scorpion did not like being (examined, kept in the sun, breathed on).

6 An **apologetic gesture** is one which shows (he is sorry to have to do it, he is cross, he is rude).

7 Why do you think he raised his tail? (To run away, to get ready to sting, to show off his beads)

8 Where does a scorpion like being best? (In the sun, out walking, in the shade, on his back)

9 Which one word in the passage tells us that the scorpion is ugly and peculiar-looking? weird

Write another word to define each of the long words below:

10 masticate ....chew/eat.... 11 renovate ....renew....

12 ludicrous ....comical.... 13 reverberate ....echo....

14 anonymous ....nameless.... 15 gigantic ....huge....

16 deficiency ....lack.... 17 tranquil ....calm/peaceful....

Complete the words in the following sentences.

18 I gue...ssed...where she was hiding.

19 Caroline was my gue....st....for the night.

20 The girl won a med....al....for lifesaving.

21 Mum told Katie not to med....dle... with the tools.

22 To make bets is to gam....ble....

23 Lambs gam....bol... in spring.

24 Dad is ....sea... ling the freezer bags with wire tags.

25 Mum decided she would paint the ....cei...ling in my bedroom.

26 The Headmaster was pleased to ....acc...ept the gift.

27 They could all go to the baths ....exc...ept William who had a cold.

Form a noun from each of the words on the left:

28 **acquaint** My sister liked the acquaintance she met at the bus stop.

29 **imagine** She used her imagination to write an excellent essay.

30 **edit** The editor of the local paper printed an account of our concert.

31 **compete** One competitor was missing at the start of the race.

32 **auction** Dad acted as auctioneer when we sold off our school jumble.

33 **employ** I work for Mr. Smith who is a very kind employer.

34 **detect** We enjoyed the film about the American detective.

Make adjectives from the following words:

35 **expense** expensive 36 **fashion** fashionable

37 **anger** angry 38 **sense** sensible

13

Underline the correct word in the brackets:

39   None of the children (are, is) going out.

40   The pen was (laying, lying) on the book.

41   Please try (to, and) think what you are going to do.

42   (Is, Are) either of these books yours?

43   Every one of you (has, have) an equal chance.

44   Maria and (me, I) will feed the cat.

45   He should (have, of) done it better.

46   Neither Tom (nor, or) Tim will go out.

Read this passage carefully and then answer the questions:

He made a small, swift sign to the others behind him, and knew, though no breath of movement told him so, that they had slipped away, right and left, to draw their ring about the place. Drem crouched motionless in the brown gloom under the yew branches, his hand clenched on the spear shaft until the knuckles shone white. His nostrils widened, and little tremors ran through his body, houndwise, as the smell of the wolf came to him down the wind ...

From *Warrior Scarlet* by Rosemary Sutcliffe

47   The others had **slipped away** means (they had fallen down, they had scattered, they had gone home).

48   His knuckles were white because (his hands were cold, it was frosty, he had hurt himself, he was pressing hard).

49   **To draw their ring** means (to surround something, to make a sketch map of a place, to tie up something).

50   **Nostrils** are part of the (hand, nose, leg, shoulder).

51   **Tremors** are (tempers, sneezes, shakings, tears).

52   His feelings are like that of a (captured wolf, hunting dog, bird of prey).

53–55   Three consecutive words in the passage are an example of alliteration. Write down these words.   small, swift, sign

Write the singular of the following words:

56	echoes	echo	57	women	woman
58	leaves	leaf	59	oases	oasis
60	geese	goose	61	media	medium
62	aircraft	aircraft			

Choose adverbs from the list on the left to best describe each verb.

63	(1) politely	The ballerina **danced**	(5)
64	(2) breathlessly	The class **listened**	(8)
65	(3) brightly	The rain **beat**	(6)
66	(4) frequently	The sun **shone**	(3)
67	(5) gracefully	The burglar **crept**	(7)
68	(6) heavily	The child **answered**	(1)
69	(7) stealthily	The boy **coughed**	(4)
70	(8) attentively	The actress **spoke**	(9)
71	(9) fluently	The athlete **finished**	(2)

Use one of these conjunctions to fill each of the spaces:

where   when   but   because   until   as   while

72 Mum got tea ready _while_ I did my homework.

73 We wanted to play tennis _but_ there were no courts available.

74 Our class went to Higham Castle _where_ we saw a ducking stool.

75 You cannot watch TV _until_ you have tidied your bedroom.

76 You must eat fish _as_ it is good for you.

77 We know you broke the window _because_ we saw you do it.

78 They were crossing the road _when_ we saw them.

Try to match the list of meanings with the words on the left. Put the correct number in each space.

79	**galley**	...(4)...	(1)	Birds are kept here.
80	**drey**	...(7)...	(2)	Art treasures are kept and shown here.
81	**sty**	...(5)...	(3)	Records are kept here.
82	**apiary**	...(8)...	(4)	A ship's kitchen.
83	**aviary**	...(1)...	(5)	Pigs are kept here.
84	**archives**	...(3)...	(6)	Experiments are made here.
85	**laboratory**	...(6)...	(7)	A squirrel's home.
86	**museum**	...(2)...	(8)	Bees are kept here.

Look carefully at the words listed below and then choose the most suitable to fill each space.

finished   closed   completed   ended   stopped   discontinued

87 The clock _stopped_ because it had not been wound.

88 The factory _discontinued_ making the kind of pen I like.

89 They _closed_ the shop at seven o'clock.

90 When we had _finished_ our work we knew we could play.

91 The fireworks were lovely and the day _ended_ happily.

92 The author was very tired when he had _completed_ his book.

Add exclamation marks or question marks to the following sentences:

93 What are you doing out there?

94 You are a nuisance. Go away!

95 I'm busy. Keep out!

96 Do you know where I put the book?

Fill in the blanks:

97 ....._Welsh_..... lamb comes from Wales.

98 ....._Tibetan_... rugs are made in Tibet.

99 Holland is the home of the ....._Dutch_.... people.

100 _Portuguese_ people come from Portugal.

Read the passage carefully, and then answer the questions. Where several possible answers are given, underline the correct answer.

Back to school – but for how long? A new class and new friends bring children into contact with new germs, and, as children have a less mature immune system, they catch twice as many colds as adults. A sore, dry throat can make children reluctant to swallow, so it's important to encourage them to drink. Help relieve their discomfort with anti-bacterial lozenges that help combat the germs which cause sore throats.

From an advertisement in *Good Housekeeping*

94	Why might children soon be away from school?	They don't like their new class, <u>they might catch bad colds</u>, they might have to change schools
95	Which word means "something that fights against germs"?	<u>antibacterial</u>
96	Which word means "Helps resist disease"?	<u>immune</u>
97	Which word means "older having finished growing"?	<u>mature</u>
98	What do you think the advertisement is for?	a book about diseases, bandages, <u>cough sweets</u>, cough medicine
99	Why would children not want to swallow?	<u>it would hurt</u>, they were naughty, they were not thirsty
100	"Reluctant" means:	impossible, available, <u>unwilling</u>, relieving

Paper 4

Put these phrases in the right sentences.
Write the numbers in the spaces provided.

(1) **again and again**　　(2) **round and round**　　(3) **odds and ends**
(4) **high and low**　　(5) **give and take**　　(6) **head and shoulders**
(7) **touch and go**　　(8) **safe and sound**　　(9) **lock and key**

1　Sue was rather selfish and her mother said she would have to learn to
　..(5)..

2　We had been out for a long time and our parents were relieved to find
　that we were ..(8)..

3　Kim had to do her work ..(1).. until she got it right.

4　We were told to tidy our desks as they were full of ..(3)..

5　We all felt happier when we knew that the burglar was under ..(9)..

6　I felt rather giddy as I had been turning ..(2)..

7　My brother is ..(6).. taller than I am.

8　We had to run to the station and it was ..(7).. if we caught the train.

9　We looked ..(4).. for the book but couldn't find it.

10–13　Read the passage and then underline all the true statements below.

The old stage-coach was rumbling along the dusty road that runs from
Maplewood to Riverboro. The day was as warm as midsummer, though
it was only the middle of May, and Mr. Jeremiah Cobb was favouring
the horses as much as possible, yet never losing sight of the fact that
he carried the mail. The hills were many, and the reins lay loosely in
his hands as he lolled back in his seat and extended one foot and leg
luxuriously over the dashboard.

From *Rebecca of Sunnybrook Farm* by K. D. Wiggin

It was a spring day

It was a summer day

Mr. Cobb was admiring the horses

Mr. Cobb was letting the horses take their time

The stage coach was carrying the mail

He kept looking at the mail to see it wasn't stolen

The road was not flat

17

Read the following carefully, and then answer the questions

Eight months ago, on Christmas Day,
he was a present for the twins,
a toy to join in all their play.

They left by car, but how long since
he cannot tell, nor when they'll come
(if ever) to make amends.

The house is blind and deaf and dumb,
the curtains drawn, the windows shut,
the doors sealed tighter than a tomb.

Even the little garden hut
is padlocked. He barks feebly at
each slowing car or passing foot.

Stretched on the WELCOME on the mat
in the front porch, he feels the hunger
gnawing inside him like a rat.

Suffers, endures, but knows no anger.

"Family Holiday" by Raymond Wilson

14 The story is about (a family holiday, Christmas Day, a neglected dog).

15 **The house is blind and deaf and dumb** means (it is a home for disabled people, there is no one there, animals are not allowed).

16 The dog is living (in the porch, in the empty house, in the shed).

17 He gets his food (from neighbours, rats, he doesn't get any).

18–19 **He barks feebly at each slowing car** means (he is too weak to bark loudly, he is barking to protect the house, he never has a loud bark, he hopes it is his family returning).

20 A dog is (not a toy, not just a Christmas present, an animal to be looked after).

Underline the word on each line which has the same meaning as the word on the left, and ring the word which has the opposite meaning.

21–22	**blame**	wrong	careless	censure	bad	praise
23–24	**elevate**	high	raise	lower	elude	bottom
25–26	**assemble**	disperse	divide	together	unite	gather
27–28	**expand**	larger	contract	smaller	increase	dispand
29–30	**least**	little	most	minimum	lot	maximum

Underline an adjective in each of the following sentences:

31   Where is your blue knapsack?   32   Four friends came to tea.

33   Ian got good marks in his test.   34   He cleans his dirty shoes.

35   Mum bought twenty stamps.   36   The small book is lost.

Use words derived from the noun in heavy type to complete the sentences.

She had the **sense** to stop.   She knew she must show **caution**.

37   She made a sensible decision.   38   She acted sensibly .

39   She acted in a cautious way.   40   She behaved cautiously.

The man committed a **crime**.   He acted with great **haste**.

41   He acted in a criminal way.   42   He acted criminally.

43   His was a hasty action.   44   He performed the deed hastily .

The infinitive is the simplest form of a verb; it usually has a **to** in front of it. Underline any infinitives below:

45   She did not know how to do the sum.

46   He thought he ought to clean the car.

47   To wash it will be better than cleaning it.

48   Who is to say what should be done.

49   She thought it was rude to ignore her.

50   She had forgotten to send Ann a birthday card.

19

Read the following carefully and then answer the questions.
Where several possible answers are given. Underline the correct answer.

A bee colony is a family community of which every individual is an integral part. The life of the honey bee colony is potentially endless; the continued survival of the colony results from the fact that young queens replace the old. The degree of social organisation in the colony is most evident in the division of labour. Tasks are assigned according to age. After performing tasks within the hive (such as cleaning, brood nursing, and comb building) a worker bee becomes, after about twenty days, an entrance guard, and finally a collector, remaining at this job until her death.

The highly integrated activities of the colony require sophisticated methods of passing information among its members. The dance of the honey bee is perhaps the most remarkable. After a bee has discovered a new source of food, she tells other bees about it by means of various dance-like movements. If the food source is near a hive, a "round" dance is performed. A "tail-wagging" dance indicates that the food source is more than 80 metres away. An upward tail-wagging run means, "The flight is towards the sun".

From *Did you know? Fascinating facts* from *Encyclopaedia Britannica*

51 What name is given to the bee in charge of the colony? Queen

52 **Division of labour** means (the bees do a lot of work, they do not do much work, the work is shared, when one bee dies another takes over).

53 The middle-aged bees do (cleaning, brood nursing, entrance guarding, comb building, collecting).

54 The older bees do (cleaning, brood nursing, entrance guarding, collecting, comb building).

55–57 The young bees do (cleaning, collecting, brood nursing, comb building, entrance guarding).

58 How do bees send messages? (By the guards, by swarming, by dancing, by buzzing).

59 If they dance a "round" dance, where will the food be? (Far away, near at hand, in the hive)

60 If the food is far afield they will (dance a "round" dance, wag their tails, turn their tails up).

61 **Every individual is an integral part** means that each bee (has to dance, has a job to do, has to pass on information, dies within twenty days).

62 In this passage, **sophisticated** means (like human beings, dressed up, complicated, silly).

Give the plurals of the following nouns:

63	mouse	mice	64	story	stories	
65	cargo	cargoes	66	thief	thieves	
67	curio	curios	68	trolley	trolleys	
69	potato	potatoes	70	piano	pianos	
71	wolf	wolves	72	valley	valleys	
73	ox	oxen	74	gas	gases	
75	roof	roofs				

Add the suffix **-ing** to each of the following words. You may have to change the spelling.

76	bite	biting	77	hit	hitting	78	write	writing	
79	beg	begging	80	pat	patting	81	give	giving	

Complete the following words by adding either **-ent** or **-ant**.

82	competent	83	consistent	84	dormant
85	intolerant	86	persistent	87	confident
88	assistant	89	superintendent	90	excellent

Complete each of the following sentences with a preposition.

91 His book is different from mine.

92 Mr. Jones is an authority on beetles.

93 That is an exception to the rule.

94 They were not allowed beyond the fence.

Use the words given on the left to complete each sentence:

95–96	**new** **knew**	Dad knew that I had bought a new pen.
97–98	**course** **coarse**	Of course I knew that the material was very coarse.
99–100	**beach** **beech**	The beech tree was in a garden quite near the beach .

Read the following carefully, and then answer the questions.
Where several possible answers are given, underline the correct answer.

Then, when the child had gone,
I was alone
In the house, suddenly grown vast. Each noise
Explained its origin away,
Animal, vegetable, mineral,
Nail, creaking board, or mouse.
But mostly there was quiet of after battle
Round the room where lay
The soldiers and the paintbox, all the toys,
Then, when I went to tidy these away,
My hands refused to serve;
My body was the house
And everything he'd touched, an exposed nerve.

"Empty House" by Stephen Spender

1   The poem is about (a mysterious house, a person wanting to tidy up after a child had gone away, <u>a person feeling lonely after the departure of a child</u>).

All things can be divided into three groups: animal, vegetable and mineral.

2   The nail is mineral

3   The creaking board is vegetable

4   The mouse is animal

5   **My hands refused to serve** means (I didn't like waiting on people, <u>I was unable to use my hands</u>, the toys were too heavy for me to lift).

6   The house seemed larger because (<u>I was alone</u>, I had put all the things away, it had been extended).

7   **Everything he'd touched, an exposed nerve** means (I was ill, I was nervous of being alone, <u>the toys brought back memories of the boy</u>).

Instead of saying **the paws of a dog** we usually say **a dog's paws**.
Do the same with the following:

8	The funnels of the ships	The ships' funnels
9	The coat of the lady	The lady's coat
10	The work of the men	The men's work
11	The cars of the teachers	The teachers' cars
12	The cat of my cousin	My cousin's cat
13	The anoraks of the children	The children's anoraks
14	The bank account of the woman	The woman's bank account
15	The guitars of the singers	The singers' guitars
16	The chair of the dentist	The dentist's chair
17	The walls of the flats	The flats' walls

In each of the following lines, underline a word which rhymes with the word on the left.

18	**heir**	weir	fair	near	leer	were
19	**sign**	reign	cane	feign	mine	wane
20	**shoal**	school	toil	whole	gruel	mule
21	**blew**	sew	go	flow	glue	glow
22	**hue**	who	though	mew	sew	low
23	**cough**	tough	cuff	laugh	bough	off
24	**quay**	fee	lay	guy	may	buy
25	**gauge**	gorge	deluge	huge	page	forge

Fill in the missing letter in each word. It may be **a**, **e** or **o**.

26	decorator	27	cellar	28	plumber
29	disaster	30	corridor	31	burglar
32	popular	33	circular	34	divisor
35	director	36	proprietor	37	partner

23

Read the following carefully, and then answer the questions.
Where several possible answers are given, underline the correct answer.

And indeed, it appeared as though her pessimism was justified. Far below, the busy city came to life. Traffic began to flow through the streets, from which arose a kind of muted and distant roar that drifted up to the two fixed to their precarious perches and tended to drown out the cries by which they sought to draw attention to themselves. On the suspension bridge, footwalkers crossed in a steady stream between Portland Street and St. Enoch's. People walked along the embankment and in the busy side streets. But no eyes turned upwards towards the sky and the top of the towers.

From *Jenny* by Paul Gallico

38   The passage is about (people stranded on the suspension bridge, danger in the streets, <u>people up a tower crying for help</u>).

39   What time of day was it? (<u>Morning</u>, noon, afternoon, evening, night)

40   **Precarious** means (picturesque, precious, <u>insecure</u>, badly built).

41   What is the opposite of **pessimism**?   <u>optimism</u>

42   How many people do we know were in trouble? (A crowd, three, <u>two</u>, one, none)

43   In the passage, which word is used to mean the same as **tried to**?
                                                                <u>sought</u>

44   **Came to life** means (babies were being born, <u>people began to move around</u>, people woke up).

45   Why did the people wish to draw attention to themselves? (They were showing off, they wanted money, <u>they wanted help</u>, they were collecting for charity)

46   People didn't look up because (<u>they didn't hear anything unusual</u>, they didn't bother, the sun was in their eyes).

47–54   Punctuate the following:

"What time are you going home?" said Jill to her brother. "I don't want to be late." "I'll go when you are ready," replied Tim.

55–62   Fill in the missing words in the passage below.

There once <u>was</u> a poor tailor, who had a son <u>called/named</u> Aladin, a careless, idle boy who would do <u>nothing</u> but play all <u>day</u> long in the streets, with little, idle boys like <u>himself</u>. One day when he <u>was</u> playing in the <u>streets</u> as usual, a stranger <u>asked</u> him his age.

Find a word derived from the word on the left to fill each space.

63	**accurate**	She worked with _accuracy_ .
64	**mercy**	He was very _merciful_ .
65	**luxury**	Their house was _luxurious_ .
66	**wise**	I was impressed by his _wisdom_ .
67	**decide**	Their _decision_ was right.
68	**sympathy**	The nurse was _sympathetic_ .
69	**fragrant**	The _fragrance_ was strong.
70	**proclaim**	He read the _proclamation_ .
71	**deliver**	When is the next postal _delivery_ ?
72	**statement**	I would like to _state_ my case.

73–80 Prefixes can be placed before words to alter their meanings. Some of the words below can have a **dis** placed in front of them, others can have a **mis**.

use, appoint, direct, colour, please, took, read, appear

DIS	MIS
colour	use
appoint	direct
please	took
appear	read

Complete each of the following sentences by writing the past tense of the word on the left.

81	**creep**	They _crept_ slowly towards her.
82	**lose**	He _lost_ his ball when he was out in the woods.
83	**speak**	The lady _spoke_ kindly to the little girl.
84	**weep**	Miranda _wept_ when her kitten died.
85	**throw**	Ian _threw_ the ball over the wall.
86	**ring**	The policewoman _rang_ the door bell.
87	**write**	They _wrote_ long essays.
88	**break**	Mum was cross when they _broke_ the plate.

Two words on each line have the same meaning. Underline those words.

89 <u>accurate</u> mark accept <u>exact</u> start
90 control <u>commence</u> continue cheap <u>begin</u>
91 often once <u>seldom</u> odd <u>rarely</u>
92 <u>trade</u> <u>commerce</u> shop cost customer
93 older order <u>previous</u> starter <u>former</u>
94 fight <u>dare</u> win <u>challenge</u> cheat
95 <u>perplex</u> pity <u>puzzle</u> game purpose

Complete the following words:

96 People at a church service — con gregation
97 People at a concert — a udience
98 People watching a football match — spe ctators
99 People on the street — c rowd
100 People taking part in a sporting event — com petitors

Read the following carefully, and then answer the questions.
Where several possible answers are given, underline the correct answer.

I take it you already know
Of **tough** and **bough** and **cough** and **dough**?
Others may stumble but not you,
On **hiccough, thorough, tough** and **through**?
Well done! And now you wish, perhaps,
To learn of less familiar traps?

Beware of **heard**, a dreadful word
That looks like **beard** and sounds like **bird**,
And **dead**: it's said like **bed**, not **bead** —
For goodness sake don't call it "**deed**"!
Watch out for **meat** and **great** and **threat**
They rhyme with **suite** and **straight** and **debt**.

A **moth** is not a **moth** in **mother**
Nor **both** in **bother, broth** in **brother**,
And **here** is not a match for **there**
Nor **dear** and **fear** for **bear** and **pear**,
And then there's **dose** and **rose** and **lose** —
Just look them up — and **goose** and **choose**,

And **cork** and **work** and **card** and **ward**
And **font** and **front** and **word** and **sword**,
And **do** and **go** and **thwart** and **cart** —
Come, come, I've hardly made a start!
A dreadful language? Man alive!
I'd mastered it when I was five!

"Hints on Pronunciation for Foreigners" by T S W

1   The poet is saying that (it is difficult to learn English, it is easy to learn
    English, foreigners should find it easy).

2   Which of the words on line 4 rhymes with **drew**?   through

3   Which of the words on the second line rhymes with **muff**?   tough

4   **Heard** rhymes with (beard, word, weird).

5   Which word does the poet rhyme with **suite**?   meat

6   Does the poet say that **dose** rhymes with **rose**? (Yes, no)

27

7   Does **thwart** rhyme with **caught**? (Yes, no)

8   Which word does the poet say rhymes with **straight**?   great

9   I'd mastered it means (I told it what to do, <u>I'd learned it thoroughly,</u>
    I couldn't speak properly when I was five).

10 One of the four words does not rhyme with the other three. Underline
    the odd one (fork, cork, <u>work</u>, pork).

Pair the verbs on the left with the adverbs on the right. Place the correct
number in the space.

11	trudged ...(5)...	12	shouted ...(7)...	(1) **soundly**	(2) **insolently**
13	ate ...(6)...	14	cried ...(10)...	(3) **tunefully**	(4) **accidentally**
15	mumbled ...(8)...	16	kissed ...(9)...	(5) **wearily**	(6) **greedily**
17	slept ...(1)...	18	sang ...(3)...	(7) **furiously**	(8) **indistinctly**
19	injured ...(4)...	20	sneered ...(2)...	(9) **lovingly**	(10) **piteously**

Fill in the spaces in the following:

21 Diana wanted to change the look of her dress so she tried dy....ein....g it red.

22 She must do her piano pract....ice.... before she can go out.

23 Tim pract....is....ed his flute every day.

24 They went to the sweet shop to buy some choc....olate....

25 The children put their toys in the cu....pboard....

26 The boys picked the conkers which had fallen from the ches....tnut....tree.

In each space, write the name of the person who "fits" the word on the left.

Example: **consult – consultant**

27	advertise	advertiser	28	music	musician
29	absent	absentee	30	admire	admirer
31	assist	assistant	32	cash	cashier
33	imitate	imitator	34	magic	magician
35	school	scholar	36	compete	competitor

Read the following carefully, and then answer the questions. Where several possible answers are given, underline the correct answer.

One watch succeeded another through the day, though how the rabbits judged the passing of time is something that civilised human beings have lost the power to feel. Creatures that have neither clocks nor books are alive to all manner of knowledge about time and weather, and about direction too, as we know from their extraordinary migratory and homing journeys. The changes in the warmth and dampness of the soil, the falling of the sunlight patches, and altering movement of the beans in the light wind, the direction and strength of the air currents along the ground – all these were perceived by the rabbit awake.

From *Watership Down* by Richard Adams

37 **One watch succeeded another** means (rabbits have a way of knowing the time, they took it in turns to stay awake on guard, they knew that time passes quickly).

38 According to the passage, which is true? (That humans and animals can judge the passing of time without clocks and books, that humans used to have this power, that neither humans nor animals have this ability).

39 Every year some creatures make a journey to other lands. What is this journey called?

.... Migration ....

40–41 A rabbit can tell the time by (looking at the sun's position, the feel of the ground, the amount of rainfall, the way the plants are growing, the way the breezes blow).

42–45 Write the following in indirect speech.

Dad, said, "I am going to mow the lawn. I hope this is the last time I will have to do it this year as I am tired of doing it."

Dad said that he was going to mow the lawn. He hoped this would be the last time he would have to do it this year as he was tired of doing it.

29

Complete the following proverbs. Write one word in each space.

46 A penny for your _thoughts_   47 A rose between two _thorns_

48 Better late than _never_   49 Blood is thicker than _water_

50 Many hands make light _work_   51 Every cloud has a silver _lining_

52 More haste, less _speed_   53 Don't put all your eggs in one _basket_

54 No news is good _news_   55 Make hay while the sun _shines_

56–62 Underline any word below which applies to both male and female.

visitor   hero   <u>waiter</u>   <u>worker</u>   <u>conductor</u>   <u>singer</u>

<u>relation</u>   widow   <u>adult</u>   mayor   <u>pupil</u>   <u>passenger</u>

Here are some words and, on the right, a list of their meanings. Write the correct number in the space.

63	to discard	(3)	(1) to put out of place
64	to discover	(6)	(2) to cease
65	to disintegrate	(5)	(3) to throw away
66	to dislocate	(1)	(4) to deface
67	to disfigure	(4)	(5) to break up into fragments
68	to discontinue	(2)	(6) to find

Underline the correct word in the brackets to complete each sentence.

69 (<u>Although</u>, Because, When) the weather was cold he felt quite warm.

70 (After, <u>During</u>, Besides) the term we learned Spanish.

71 We were lost and couldn't do much (while, <u>except</u>, because) hope they would find us.

72 Ranjit said that he would write to the newspaper (<u>about</u>, for, with) our Jumble Sale.

73 Our teacher said that we could divide the cake (between, with, <u>among</u>) all the class.

74 (When, Although, <u>Because</u>) she couldn't swim she wore water wings in the sea.

75 I will share the remainder of the sweets (among, <u>between</u>, with) the twins.

Form nouns from the verbs on the left:

76 **applaud**   The _applause_ was deafening.

77 **provide**   They bought the _provisions_ at the supermarket.

78	**enter**	They couldn't find the <u>entrance</u> to the caves.
79	**choose**	They had the <u>choice</u> of going to the seaside or to a farm.
80	**advertise**	The <u>advertisement</u> said that the concert started at 7.30 p.m.
81	**perform**	The <u>performance</u> of the school play was really excellent.
82	**bewilder**	The child's <u>bewilderment</u> was plain to see.
83	**destroy**	The army was responsible for the <u>destruction</u> of the bridge.

Fill each space with either "past" or "passed".

84 She walked <u>past</u> the church.

85 Dinah <u>passed</u> the exam with honours.

86 The man <u>passed</u> her the plate.

87 In the <u>past</u> ladies wore crinolines.

88 During the <u>past</u> term you have worked well.

89 He ran <u>past</u> the pillar-box.

90 She <u>passed</u> the old house on the way to school.

Can you match the animal with the noise it makes? Write the number in the space.

91	elephant	(5)	(1)	**hisses**
92	hound	(3)	(2)	**howls**
93	turkey	(7)	(3)	**bays**
94	frog	(9)	(4)	**gibbers**
95	snake	(1)	(5)	**trumpets**
96	sheep	(8)	(6)	**hums**
97	mouse	(10)	(7)	**gobbles**
98	bee	(6)	(8)	**bleats**
99	wolf	(2)	(9)	**croaks**
100	ape	(4)	(10)	**squeaks**

Complete the following similes:

1 as alike as two peas
2 as blind as a bat
3 as cool as a cucumber
4 as easy as pie
5 as good as gold
6 as heavy as lead
7 as lively as a cricket
8 as mad as a hatter

Below are ten pairs of words: some have opposite meanings and some have similar ones. Put them in the right columns.

vacant/empty   **absence/presence**   **tranquil/peaceful**   **option/choice**

few/many   **seldom/often**   **caution/care**   **coarse/fine**

famous/noted   **here/there**

Similar   **Opposite**

9 vacant/empty   10 absence/presence
11 tranquil/peaceful   12 here/there
13 option/choice   14 coarse/fine
15 famous/noted   16 few/many
17 caution/care   18 seldom/often

Can you complete the following expressions?

19 My brother is greedy; he always wants the lion's share.

20 Caroline passed her music exam with flying colours.

21 Mum said that the cake wasn't a patch on what she could make.

22 There was one fly in the ointment – we would miss our tea!

23 Tony was so excited he was like a cat on hot bricks.

24 Mr. Brown said that there was too much horse play.

25 She was lazy and only worked by fits and starts.

26 Dad didn't believe me; he said it was a cock and bull story.

32

Use the following words to fill the spaces below:

gossip   **lecture**   **talk**   **conversation**   **interview**   **speech**

27 Before he presented the prizes Sir John Short made a ....speech.....

28 On T V we saw Terry Logan ...interview... some pop stars.

29 I overheard a very interesting ...conversation... between two ladies.

30 On the bus we heard some ....gossip.... about Jan's friend.

31 In the Town Hall there was a ....lecture.... on South Africa.

32 Our class listened to a very interesting ....talk.... on wild flowers.

In each space, write the part of speech of the word in heavy type.

33 Close the **back** door.   adjective

34 We said we would **back** Hotspot to win the Derby.   verb

35 Dad's got a pain in his **back**.   noun

36 Come **back** soon.   adverb

Write the following in direct speech:

      Mum said she would buy me a new dress.
37 Mum said, "I will buy you a new dress."

      Miss Brown said that if I got my sums right she would give me a star.
38 Miss Brown said, "If you get your sums right I will give you a star."

      Charlotte said that she must practise her recorder.
39 Charlotte said, "I must practise my recorder."

      Kim told Mia that he didn't want to play tennis.
40 Kim said to Mia, "I don't want to play tennis."

An adverb describes a verb. Underline the adverbs below:

41 She walked <u>slowly</u> to school today.

42 Ian had a large appetite, and ate his meal <u>greedily</u>.

43 Rachel wrote the invitations to her party <u>neatly</u>.

44 She watched <u>intently</u> as the T.V. programme was interesting.

45 <u>Softly</u> she sang the lilting tune.

46 She got up <u>early</u> as it was her birthday.

47 He lifted the kitten <u>carefully</u> and put it in the basket.

Read the following carefully, and then answer the questions. Where several possible answers are given, underline the correct answer.

They paddle with staccato feet
In powder-pools of sunlight,
Small blue busybodies
Strutting like fat gentlemen
With hands clasped
Under their swallowtail coats;
And, as they stump about,
Their heads like tiny hammers
Tap at imaginary nails
In non-existent walls.
Elusive ghosts of sunshine
Slither down the green gloss
Of their necks an instant, and are gone.

Summer hangs drugged from sky to earth
In limpid fathoms of silence:
Only warm dark dimples of sound
Slide like slow bubbles
From the contented throats.

Raise a casual hand —
With one quick gust
They fountain into air.

"Pigeons" by Richard Kell

48 **Staccato feet** are ones which (walk heavily, make short, sharp noises, are many coloured).

49 A **busybody** is (a swarming bee, a housewife, an officious person).

50 A **swallowtail coat** is (a coat worn on formal occasions, the plumage of a swallow, a many-coloured coat).

51 The poet says that they looked as if they were hammering. What did he think they were pretending to use for this? (Feet, bodies, nails, heads, coats)

52 Rays of sunshine make their necks appear to be (blue, green, non-existent, dark).

53 To **strut** is to (swagger, slither, limp, stutter, slide).

54 **Limpid** means (dark, not able to walk properly, sliding, ghostly, transparent).

55 Which word is used to describe the movement of the birds when frightened?

fountain

34

Use the words below to fill the spaces:

staff   **troop**   **posse**   **punnet**   **galaxy**   **string**   **gang**   **chest**

56   A gang of labourers was resurfacing the road.

57   We were given a punnet of strawberries.

58   The night was clear and we could see a galaxy of stars.

59   The teaching staff attended the meeting.

60   He put it in the chest of drawers.

61   On the film we saw a troop of monkeys.

62   Outside the hall there was a posse of policemen.

63   She was wearing a pretty string of beads.

64–68   Underline any word below which can apply to male or female.

<u>comrade</u>   wizard   sculptor   <u>cousin</u>   <u>orphan</u>

<u>traveller</u>   barmaid   <u>parent</u>   shepherd   madam

On each line, underline the word which is the same part of speech as the word on the left.

69	**well**	good	pretty	sick	<u>badly</u>	wanting
70	**go**	quickly	goat	it	for	<u>slither</u>
71	**chair**	<u>seat</u>	sit	rest	lazy	comfortable
72	**silk**	soft	woollen	lacy	<u>worm</u>	grew
73	**when**	time	place	<u>where</u>	town	hour
74	**blue**	dress	bonnet	sea	picture	<u>ugly</u>
75	**and**	sand	boat	badly	<u>but</u>	cut

Complete the following expressions by writing a preposition in each space.

76   He climbed over the gate with ease.

77   Mark corresponds with two penfriends.

78   Granny is suffering from arthritis.

79   We walked slowly along the river bank.

80   Her paper was hidden under the pile of books.

81   Keep your head above the water when learning to swim.

82   I put it by/near the radiator.

83   We waited for the bus.

One word in the brackets is connected with the words on the left. Underline it.

84 margin rim border   (pattern, <u>edge</u>, design)

85 help assist support   (hinder, refuse, <u>aid</u>)

86 speed rush hurry   (<u>hasten</u>, road, driver)

87 stain blot spot   (<u>smudge,</u> iron, wash)

88 sweater jumper pullover   (coat, trousers, <u>cardigan</u>)

89 netball hockey rounders   (tennis, <u>football,</u> badminton)

90 shoe slipper boot   (sock, foot, <u>sandal</u>)

Underline the correct word in the brackets.

91 Dad told Sarah and (I, <u>me</u>) to go to bed.

92 Sally and (<u>I</u>, me) were given some money.

93 Miss Black said that Robin and (<u>I</u>, me) had done well.

94 The sweets were to be shared between Caroline and (I, <u>me</u>).

95 Mr. Roberts asked Philip and (I, <u>me</u>) to change places.

96–100 Punctuate the following:

"Have you fed the rabbit, Vicky?" asked Mum.

Read the following carefully, and then answer the questions. Where several possible answers are given, underline the correct answer.

The week before Christmas, when the snow seemed to lie thickest, was the moment for carol-singing; and when I think back to those nights it is to the crunch of snow and to the lights of the lanterns on it. Carol-singing in my village was a special tithe for the boys; the girls had little to do with it. Like haymaking, blackberrying, stone-clearing, and wishing-people-a-happy-Easter, it was one of our seasonal perks.

By instinct we knew just when to begin it; a day too soon and we should have been unwelcome, a day too late and we should have received lean looks from people whose bounty was already exhausted. When the true moment came, exactly balanced, we recognised it and were ready ...

From *Cider with Rosie* by Laurie Lee

1 A **tithe** used to be tax. Here it means (a ticket, <u>a gift</u>, a song).

2 **Seasonal perks** are (part-time jobs, helping on the farm, <u>money given at certain times</u>).

3 Which seasonal festivals are mentioned in this passage?
Christmas   Easter

4 **Lean looks** are (<u>looks which say "No money"</u>, looks which say "No food", cross expressions, clean faces).

5 Which word means **generosity**?   bounty

6 **Instinct** means (<u>impulse</u>, teaching, timing, intelligence).

7 How many things did the boys do without the girls?   5 things

Underline the correct word in the brackets.

8 The bunch of bananas (<u>was,</u> were) very big.

9 The apples (was, <u>were</u>) rosy and ripe.

10 The sweets (was, <u>were</u>) very sticky.

11 The bag of satsumas (<u>was,</u> were) nearly empty.

12 None of the girls (<u>is,</u> are) going to the match.

13 The boys (is, <u>are</u>) going out to do their shopping.

Give the singular form of each of the following words:

14	opportunities	opportunity	15	halves	half
16	cacti	cactus	17	solos	solo
18	canoes	canoe	19	puppies	puppy
20	salmon	salmon	21	wives	wife

Underline the word which has the same meaning as the word on the left, and put a ring round the word which has an opposite meaning.

22–23	**labour**	men	fun	<u>work</u>	job	(leisure)
24–25	**burnish**	heat	<u>polish</u>	dull	(tarnish)	bright
26–27	**arrest**	(release)	attack	assault	suffer	<u>detain</u>
28–29	**answer**	test	<u>reply</u>	(question)	mark	complete
30–31	**final**	finish	<u>ultimate</u>	complete	(first)	start

Fill each space with a noun derived from the word on the left.

32 **divide** It was an unfair division.

33 **laugh** They heard hearty laughter.

34 **resemble** There was a strong resemblance between the two sisters.

35 **invite** She received an invitation to the party.

36 **act** It was a very kind action.

Add suffixes (either **-able** or **-ful**) to the following words. Be careful of the spelling!

37 love   lovable   38 use   useful   39 plenty plentiful

40 wonder wonderful   41 value valuable   42 laugh   laughable

43 right   rightful   44 power powerful   45 work   workable

Some words are missing at the end of some of the lines of this poem. So that you can complete the poem it will help you to know that the following lines rhyme:

2 and 4; 3 and 5; 7, 8 and 9; 11 and 12; 13 and 15; 14 and 16

The missing words are: **do field mind trains parade find plains end view**

In the middle of countries far from hills and sea
46 Are the little places one passes by in trains

And never stops at; where the skies extend
47 Uninterrupted, and the level plains

48 Stretch green and yellow and green without an end

And behind the glass of their Grand Express
Folk yawn away a province through,
49 With nothing to think of, nothing to do

50 Nothing even to look at – never a view

In this damned wilderness,
51 But I look out of the window and find

52 Much to satisfy the mind

Mark how the furrows, formed and wheeled
In a motion orderly and staid,
53 Sweep as we pass across the field

54 Like a drilled army on parade

What names are given to the following?

55 A road on which you are not allowed to stop, park or turn round
    motorway

56 A road lined with trees   avenue

57 A road which avoids going through a town   by-pass

58 A road on which you may travel in one direction only   <u>one-way street</u>

59 A private road leading to a house   <u>drive</u>

60 A place where pedestrians may cross a busy road   <u>zebra crossing</u>

61 An **audition** is (a free show, <u>a test,</u> a party).

62–65 The dogs must (<u>not be nervous</u>, not go on the stage, not make a noise, <u>be able to do things "in time"</u>, be able to sing, <u>look well groomed</u>, look funny, <u>be good looking</u>).

66 The audition is held (at home, in the Production Office, <u>on the stage</u>, outside).

67 The time of the test was (morning, <u>mid-day</u>, evening, by appointment).

68 To find out more you should (go to the theatre, go on the stage, <u>phone the number given</u>, write a letter).

> **WEST END SHOW**
> **seeks**
>
> attractive
>
> # DOG
>
> **(either sex)**
>
> OPEN AUDITION ON-STAGE
>
> 12 Noon Monday May 12
>
> ESSENTIAL to all applicants:–
>
> NO Stage-fright. Good sense of rhythm, clean grooming an advantage.
>
> All enquiries ring Production Office
>
> Tel: 0427918

Match the two columns below.

69	A stud of	...(8)...	(1) **herring**
70	A crew of	...(5)...	(2) **dancers**
71	A herd of	...(6)...	(3) **insects**
72	A flock of	...(10)...	(4) **lions**
73	A band of	...(7)...	(5) **sailors**
74	A plague of	...(3)...	(6) **cattle**
75	A litter of	...(9)...	(7) **musicians**
76	A shoal of	...(1)...	(8) **horses**
77	A pride of	...(4)...	(9) **puppies**
78	A troupe of	...(2)...	(10) **sheep**

94-100 Can you match these words and their meanings? Write the right number in each of the spaces provided.

monochrome	3	(1) a single rail track
monogram	5	(2) a series of sounds of the same pitch
monolith	7	(3) a single colour: black and white
monologue	6	(4) a word of one syllable
monorail	1	(5) design using initials of a name
monosyllable	4	(6) a sketch performed by one actor
monotone	2	(7) one large block of stone

Read the following carefully, and then answer the questions. Where several possible answers are given, underline the correct answer.

Hide of a leopard and hide of a deer,
And eyes of a baby calf,
Sombre and large and crystal clear,
And a comical back that is almost sheer
Has the absurd giraffe.

A crane all covered with hide and hair
Is the aslant giraffe,
So cleverly mottled with many a square
That even the jungle is unaware
Whether a pair or a herd are there,
Or possibly one giraffe,
Or possibly only half.

If you saw him stoop and straddle and drink
He would certainly make you laugh,
He would certainly make you laugh, I think
With his head right down on the water's brink,
Would the invert giraffe,
The comical, knock-kneed, angular, crock-kneed
Anyhow built giraffe!

"The Giraffe" by Geoffrey Dearmer

1 **Hide of a leopard and hide of a deer** means (the animal's skin resembles that of a leopard and a deer, he is afraid of these animals, he builds his shelter as they do).

2–4 His eyes are (sad, crossed, small, large, very clear, dull).

5 The giraffe's neck is likened to a (slant, square, leopard, deer, crane).

6 When an animal is difficult to see in the jungle it is (hiding, camouflaged, painted, stooping, extinct).

7 The movements of a giraffe are (awkward, graceful, mottled, slow, clever).

You can make some words have an opposite meaning by adding a prefix such as **dis-, ir-, un-, in-, im-,** or **il-**. Use these to give the words below an opposite meaning.

8	lock *unlock*	9	polite *impolite*	10	agree *disagree*
11	capable *incapable*	12	regular *irregular*	13	cover *uncover*

14–17 Complete the poem by filling in the rhyming words. Then answer the questions.

In the far corner,
close by the swings
every morning
a blackbird *sings*.

His bill's so yellow
His coat's so *black*
that makes a *fellow*
whistle back.

Ann – my daughter,
thinks that *he*
Sings for us two
especially.

From *The Blackbird* by Humbert Wolfe

18 How many verbs are there in the first verse? *1*

19–21 Name the nouns in the second verse
bill, coat, fellow

22 What relation is the poet to Ann? *father*

Below are some expressions. Try to pair them with the list of meanings.

23	Lock, stock and barrel	*(3)*	(1)	To be caught committing a crime
24	At the eleventh hour	*(5)*	(2)	To keep calm
25	To see the light	*(7)*	(3)	Everything
26	To put one's shoulder to the wheel	*(6)*	(4)	To confess
27	To be caught redhanded	*(1)*	(5)	At the last moment
28	To make a clean breast of	*(4)*	(6)	To work hard in order to succeed
29	To keep one's head	*(2)*	(7)	To understand

30 A person who looks after engines is an engineer

31 A person who looks after machines is a mechanic

32 A person who works in a library is a librarian

33 A person who goes on foot is a pedestrian

34 A person who sells magazines and newspapers is a newsagent

35 A person who keeps a flower shop is a florist

36 A person who mends burst pipes is a plumber

Write the verbs in heavy type in the past tense.

Today we **go** to the museum.

37 Yesterday we _went_ to the museum.

We **drink** our milk during morning break.

38 We _drank_ our milk during morning break.

They **throw** the ball over the wall.

39 They _threw_ the ball over the wall.

I **wear** my new jeans today.

40 I _wore_ my new jeans today.

Tom **shakes** the trees to make the apples drop.

41 Tom _shook_ the trees to make the apples drop.

I **find** that I **can** do it.

42–43 I _found_ that I _could_ do it.

The dogs **steal** the meat.

44 The dogs _stole_ the meat.

Below are the names of some young humans, animals, birds and plants. Can you list them in the columns?

| toddler | cub | owlet | leveret | child | gosling |
| sapling | baby | fawn | cygnet | shoot | seedling |

	Humans		**Animals**		**Birds**		**Plant life**
45	toddler	46	cub	47	owlet	48	sapling
49	child	50	fawn	51	cygnet	52	shoot
53	baby	54	leveret	55	gosling	56	seedling

45

Underline two words in the brackets which are connected with the word on the left.

57–58	**chair**	(foot, <u>leg</u>, hand, finger, <u>arm</u>)
59–60	**eye**	(<u>brow</u>, frown, <u>lash</u>, strike, watch)
61–62	**nose**	(mouth, <u>nostril</u>, ear, <u>bridge</u>, brow)
63–64	**hair**	(sweep, <u>slide</u>, glide, animal, <u>brush</u>)
65–66	**table**	(<u>top</u>, bottom, side, paper, <u>cloth</u>)
67–68	**shoe**	(sock, hose, glove, <u>lace</u>, <u>buckle</u>)
69–70	**knife**	(trowel, axe, <u>blade</u>, shovel, <u>handle</u>)

71–77   Read the passage below carefully, and then underline the statements that are true.

It was a most beautiful morning. The white clouds seemed playful and benign. The waters of the river went over the weir like a flow of silk and emptied placidly, a short distance farther on, into the sea. Many small, brightly coloured pleasure boats were tied up along the near bank, waiting for the tourists to get out of their beds.

The boy paid not the least attention to those real boats. Standing on the ramp leading into the river, he sailed his own boat. It was a short piece of rough timber, the front of which he had shaped very crudely into a sort of bow.

From *The Kiss* by Walter Mackem

The boy was in the country
<u>It describes a holiday resort</u>

<u>The boy had a roughly made boat</u>

The boy had a pleasure boat
The boy admired the pleasure boats
<u>The boy had made his boat himself</u>

<u>A weir is a kind of dam</u>

The boy watched the vistitors in their boats
<u>It was early in the morning</u>

A ramp is a kind of pleasure boat
<u>A ramp is a sloping pathway</u>

<u>The river flowed smoothly</u>

78–79   Name two words in the passage that denote an atmosphere of peace:
benign   placidly

Underline the correct word in the brackets.

80 None of the children (are, <u>is</u>) allowed in the sea.

81 All of you but one (<u>have</u>, has) brothers.

82 Neither of the children (are, <u>is</u>) from this town.

83 All the children (<u>are</u>, is) having a hamburger.

84 Which of you three (are, <u>is</u>) going to do it?

85 None of you (are, <u>is</u>) eleven years old.

Put these words in the correct column.

yellow   energy   expect   caught   danger   met   uncertainty
drown   foolish   water   helped   real   reality   carefree
artificial

Nouns		Verbs		Adjectives	
86	reality	87	expect	88	carefree
89	uncertainty	90	caught	91	yellow
92	energy	93	drown	94	foolish
95	water	96	helped	97	artificial
98	danger	99	met	100	real

Read the following carefully, and then answer the questions. Where several possible answers are given, underline the correct answer.

The guards were drinking and laughing by the fire in their hut and did not hear the footsteps of the scouts. Their astonishment was enormous when Thorin Oakenshield stepped in through the door.

"Who are you and what do you want?" they shouted, leaping to their feet and groping for their weapons.

"Thorin, son of Thrain, son of Thror King under the Mountain!" said the dwarf in a loud voice, and he looked it, in spite of his torn clothes and draggled hood. The gold gleamed on his neck and waist; his eyes were dark and deep.

"I have come back. I wish to see the Master of your town!"

"If you come in peace, lay down your arms," said the captain.

From *The Hobbit* by J. R. R. Tolkien

79-80 The guards were (watchful, alert, unhappy, <u>slack</u>, diligent, <u>surprised</u>).

81 To **grope** is to (<u>search blindly</u>, pick up, call out, be ready to fight).

82 The guards leapt to their feet so that (they could greet their guest, <u>they were ready to fight</u>, they showed what good guards they were).

83 **And he looked it** means (he stared at the other man, he glanced round the hut, he looked like a tramp, <u>he looked important</u>).

84 To **lay down your arms** is to (sit comfortably, <u>put down your weapons</u>, relax, get ready to fight).

85 **Draggled** is (waterproof, wool-lined, threadbare, <u>wet and dirty</u>).

86 His necklace and belt were made of ...<u>gold</u>...

87 Was Thorin a stranger to the area? (Yes, We are not told, <u>No</u>)

One word on each line is different from the others. Underline that word.

88	forecast	<u>bulletin</u>	anticipate	expect	predict
89	diminish	lessen	decrease	<u>size</u>	shrink
90	multitude	mob	crowd	host	<u>guest</u>
91	elevate	<u>escalator</u>	lift	raise	heighten
92	<u>solve</u>	suppose	guess	suspect	surmise
93	paint	sketch	<u>pad</u>	draw	design

Paper 10

Read the following carefully, then answer the questions. Where several possible answers are given, underline the correct answer.

I should like to rise and go
Where the golden apples grow,
Where below another sky
Parrot islands anchored lie,
Lonely Crusoe's building boats,
Where in sunshine reaching out
Eastern cities, miles about,
Are with mosque and minaret
Among sandy gardens set,
And the rich goods from near and far
Hang for sale in the bazaar.

From *I should like to rise and go* by R. L. Stevenson

1 The countries that the writer would like to visit (are like our own, are cold, are hot, have little sunshine, have a lot of sunshine).

2 Name the place of worship that is mentioned. mosque

3 Name the kind of market that is mentioned. bazaar

4 A **cockatoo** is a kind of (hen, partridge, parrot, pheasant).

5 **Lonely Crusoes** are (people who are not friendly, people living in remote places, people trying to get back to civilisation).

6 A **minaret** is (a small church, a boat, a tower, a market place).

7 **Below another sky** is (a place on the moon, somewhere with a different climate, somewhere in the southern hemisphere).

Complete these similes.

8	Like water off a	...(2)...	(1)	March hare
9	Like a bull in a	...(5)...	(2)	duck's back
10	As fit as a	...(4)...	(3)	church mouse
11	As mad as a	...(1)...	(4)	fiddle
12	As poor as a	...(3)...	(5)	china shop

48

Add the suffix **-ing** to each of the following words. You may have to alter the spelling of some of the words.

13 hop hopping   14 beat beating   15 drive driving

16 lie lying   17 forget forgetting   18 skid skidding

19 become becoming   20 beg begging   21 come coming

Write two words which rhyme with the word in heavy type. You are given some of the letters:

hum	**horn**	**herd**	**fraught**
22 crumb	24 dawn	26 third	28 port
23 dumb	25 morn	27 curd	29 aught

law	**where**	**floor**
30 tore	32 lair	34 core
31 door	33 mare	35 paw

Choose one of the conjunctions below to fill each space.

where   **because**   **or**   **whether**   **unless**   **if**   **until**

36 I intend to go whether you like it or not.

37 We had to wait in the rain until the bus came.

38 You won't finish your drawing unless you hurry up.

39 You must make the cake because it is your party.

40 They went to Switzerland where there was plenty of snow.

41 Will you come for a walk or do you want to watch television?

42 The playground will be much better if it is resurfaced during the holidays.

Give each of the words below an opposite meaning by adding one of these prefixes.

in-   **un-**   **il-**   **im-**   **ir-**   **non-**   **mis-**   **dis-**

43 patient im patient   44 legible il legible

45 responsible ir responsible   46 contented dis contented

47 informed mis informed   48 sense non sense

49 considerate in considerate   50 certain un certain

Read the following carefully, and then answer the questions. Where several possible answers are given, underline the correct answer.

Old tufts of wool on the grass
The clipping's over. But once again
The small quicksilver flock come pouring
Down from the hill towards the pen.

The dogs run on the ruined walls,
Swinging their tongues, their minds all sheep,
The zinc bath winks, the stirrup pump
Guzzles the primrose one foot deep.

Then out they come bounding high over
Nothing at all, and ramble on
The shining crags – not quicksilver
But golden fleeces, everyone.

From "Spraying sheep" by Norman MacCaig

51 The dogs are (enjoying running around the field, trying to lead the sheep to be shorn, trying to round them up to be washed).

52 Why were tufts of wool on the grass? (They had been dropped there, they came off the sheep when shorn, the sheep were moulting)

53 The dogs' minds were **all sheep** means (they thought like sheep, they were only thinking about the sheep, they were dreaming of the sheep).

54 **The zinc bath winks** means (the bath is ready for the sheep, someone had been doing some washing, the children were playing with it).

55 How do we know the sheep were happy? (They had golden fleeces, they bounded high over nothing at all, they swung their tongues, they rambled on)

56 What colour were the sheep after they had been bathed? (White, black, golden, silver)

Use the words below to fill the spaces.

altar, alter, dairy, diary, sauce, source, practice, practise

57 She wrote a full account of it in her ...diary....

58 They bought some cheese at the ...dairy....

59 We all like apple sauce with pork.

60 The source of the River Dee is in north Wales.

50

61 The team must _practise_ their bowling.

62 I must do some _practice_.

63 There were beautiful lilies on the _altar_ .

64 Miss Bell must _alter_ her timetable.

65 **north** is to **south** as **ebb** is to _flow_

66 **stop** is to **red** as **go** is to _green_

67 **day** is to **night** as **odd** is to _even_

68 **simple** is to **easy** as **hard** is to _difficult_

69 **come** is to **arrive** as **go** is to _depart_

70 **Aware** is to **unaware** as **necessary** is to _unnecessary_

71 **inside** is to **internal** as **outside** is to _external_

In each space, write the superlative form of the word on the left.

72 **good**   This is the _best_ party I have ever been to.

73 **long**   The _longest_ road is in the Pennines.

74 **many**   _Most_ of you have brought your wellingtons.

75 **tasty**   Your mince pies are the _tastiest_ I have ever had.

76 **wonderful** It was quite the _most wonderful_ place I have ever visited.

77 **little**   Be very quiet! Make the _least_ noise possible.

78 **bad**   It was the _worst_ storm for many years.

Write one word in place of the group of words in heavy type.

79 They were delighted to be able to talk to the **person who wrote the book.** _author_

80 The children put the **exercise books, pencils and rubbers** in the cupboard. _stationery_

81 Peter **said he was sorry** for what he had done. _apologised_

82 The weather has improved **during the last day or two.** _recently_

83 The children who were **at school that day** put up the decorations. _present_

84-90 Underline the words below which can apply to either male or female.

master   <u>owner</u>   bride   aunt   <u>shopkeeper</u>   <u>animal</u>   men

<u>teacher</u>   headmaster   <u>pupil</u>   boy   <u>tourist</u>   daughter   <u>person</u>

Put the following words in alphabetical order.

schooner   scheme   scholar   school   sceptre

91   (1) sceptre   92   (2) scheme   93   (3) scholar

94   (4) school   95   (5) schooner

Fill each space with a word derived from the word on the left.

96   **essence**   It is   essential   to understand First Aid.

97   **appear**   The difference between them is not   apparent   .

98   **vigour**   The athlete's movements were   vigorous   .

99   **rhythm**   The conductor's arm moved   rhythmically   .

100 **reconcile**   After the argument there was a   reconciliation .

52

Paper II

Read the following carefully, and then answer the questions. When several possible answers are given, underline the correct answer.

Dear Madam, you have seen the play;
I never saw it till today,
You know the details of the plot,
But, let me tell you, I do not.
The author seeks to keep from me
The murderer's identity,
And you are not a friend of his
If you keep shouting who it is.
The actors in their funny way
Have several funny things to say,
But they do not amuse me more
If you have said them just before.
The merit of the drama lies,
I understand, in some surprise;
But the surprise must now be small
Since you have just foretold it all.
The lady you have brought with you
Is, I infer, a half-wit too,
But I can understand the piece
Without assistance from your niece.
In short, foul woman, it would suit
Me just as well if you were mute,
In fact, to make my meaning plain,
I trust you will not speak again.
And – may I add one human touch?
Don't breathe upon my neck so much.

"At the Theatre" by A. P. Herbert

1–2 The speaker is (polite, annoyed, amused, speechless, sarcastic, affectionate).

3 What kind of play were they watching? (A comedy, a historical play, a murder, a ballet)

4 The person being spoken to is (a woman, a man, a girl, his niece).

5 The speaker did not like (not knowing what was going to happen, hearing what was going to happen next, the fact that the play was not interesting).

6   The speaker also objected to the lady (being restless, puffing smoke over him, <u>breathing down his neck</u>, not being a friend of the author).

7   It would please the speaker if the lady were (an actress, a friend of the author, all alone, <u>unable to speak</u>).

Match the objects listed on the left of the page with the noises they make which are on the right. Put the number in the space provided.

8	corks	...(3)...	(1)	**jingle**
9	drums	...(9)...	(2)	**patters**
10	clocks	...(5)...	(3)	**pop**
11	water	...(7)...	(4)	**creak**
12	whips	...(10)...	(5)	**tick**
13	telephones	...(8)...	(6)	**slam**
14	coins	...(1)...	(7)	**laps**
15	stairs	...(4)...	(8)	**ring**
16	rain	...(2)...	(9)	**beat**
17	doors	...(6)...	(10)	**crack**

Make nouns from the words on the left to complete the sentences.

18 **punish**   I do not believe in capital punishment.

19 **fragrant**   The fragrance of the rose was beautiful.

20 **arrive**   The arrival of the pop singer at the airport was delayed because it was foggy.

21 **long**   Sarah said that her trousers were not the right length.

22 **conclude**   At the conclusion of the concert we rushed to get home.

23 **assist**   Dad asked Tom for his assistance.

Underline the correct word in the brackets.

24 She never said (nothing, <u>anything</u>, something).

25 It is no good (<u>their</u>, there, them) going.

26 He was (stood, <u>standing</u>) at the bus stop.

27 The choir (<u>sang</u>, sung) beautifully.

28   It is useless (me, <u>my</u>) doing it.

29   When he fell he hurt (<u>himself</u>, his-self).

30   The boys had frightened him and he (<u>was</u>, were) crying.

A long stretch of shore – shingle edged by sand and intersected at short intervals with black groynes running down into the water – a scene, in fact, so like that of his afternoon's walk that, in the absence of any landmark, it could not be distinguished therefrom. The light was obscure, conveying an impression of gathering storm, late winter evening and slight cold rain. On this bleak stage at first no actor was visible. Then, in the distance, a bobbing, black object appeared; a moment more and it was a man running, jumping, clambering over the groynes, and every few seconds looking eagerly back. The nearer he came the more obvious it was that he was not only anxious, but even terribly frightened, though his face was not to be distinguished. He was, moreover, almost at the end of his strength.

From *Whistle and I'll come for you* by M. R. James

31–38   Underline the statements which are true.

<u>There was a long beach</u>

The beach was sandy
Groynes keep the sand off the beach
<u>It was dull and cold and wet</u>

Groynes are banks of dirty sand
<u>There was not a great distance between the groynes</u>

<u>At first the beach appeared to be deserted</u>

<u>The beach was mostly made up of pebbles</u>

The man's face was unremarkable
His face showed that he was suffering
<u>Along the beach were several breakwaters</u>

<u>The man appeared to be exhausted</u>

<u>It seemed that the man was being chased</u>

Underline the word which has the same meaning as the word on the left, and put a ring round the one which has an opposite meaning.

39–40	**unnatural**	odd	<u>artificial</u>	painted	(real) plain
41–42	**agitate**	(calm)	cross	amiable	rude <u>excite</u>
43–44	**courteous**	lovely	<u>polite</u>	(rude)	bad quiet
45–46	**protect**	<u>guard</u>	insure	save	hurt (attack)
47–48	**tedious**	(interesting)	lengthy	<u>boring</u>	bright short

55

Complete the sentences below using words from the column on the right of the page. Write the number of the word in the given space.

49   They were ...(6)... to go to the sweet shop.

(1) **desert**

50   They were told not to read ...(5)... .

(2) **dessert**

51   "Have you done your piano ...(7)... today?"

(3) **throne**

52   "I must ...(8)... my flute."

(4) **thrown**

53   "You will need more ...(10)... to write the letters."

(5) **aloud**

54   The train was ...(9)...; they need not have hurried.

(6) **allowed**

55   We had peaches and cream for our ...(2)... .

(7) **practice**

56   The Sahara ...(1)... is in Africa.

(8) **practise**

57   Queen Elizabeth II ascended the ...(3)... in 1952.

(9) **stationary**

58   The ball was ...(4)... through the window.

(10) **stationery**

Fit the words on the right into the sentences by writing the number of the word in the space:

59   We went to the ...(4)... to collect the medicine.

(1) **disconnected**

60   Julie was a friendly girl – she had a pleasant ...(6).

(2) **disputed**

61   We couldn't watch television because the set had

been ...(1)... .

(3) **distinctive**

62   The children ...(8)... after school.

(4) **dispensary**

63   Some of the class ...(7)... the teacher.

(5) **district**

64   There was a ...(9)... in the street outside.

(6) **disposition**

65   The tennis player ...(2)... the decision.

(7) **disobeyed**

66   The vicar ...(10)... the hymn sheets.

(8) **dispersed**

67   The curry they made had a ...(3)... flavour.

(9) **disturbance**

68   In the ...(5)... there were several bookshops.

(10) **distributed**

Fill each space with a word derived from the word on the left.

69	**behave**	We watched the behaviour of the kittens with amusement.
70	**advertise**	We saw an advertisement for coffee on television.
71	**benefit**	Swimming is beneficial exercise.
72	**pity**	The baby was crying pitifully.
73	**interrupt**	Take the phone off the hook; I don't want any interruptions.

Complete the following words with either **ie** or **ei**.

| 74 | foreign | 75 | believe | 76 | achieve | 77 | conceited |
| 78 | neighbour | 79 | audience | 80 | height | 81 | ceiling |

Read the following carefully, and then answer the questions. Where several possible answers are given, underline the correct answer.

What animal sports ears like a horse, hind feet like a rhinoceros, a body like a pig's and an elephantine trunk, and is more agile than most dogs despite its bulk? Give up? The beast is a tapir, one of the least known creatures on earth.

Along with their close relatives, horses and rhinoceroses, tapirs are descendants of prehistoric odd-toed hoofed animals, of which there were once more than 150 kinds. Tapirs' eyes are tiny and their vision is poor; their brains, like those of many primitive animals, are small for their body size. Great lumps of creatures, solid as brick walls, with bull-like necks, short powerful legs and stubby tails, they swim with surprising speed and grace, and can stay submerged for a long time.

From *The Creatures Time forgot* by Emily and Ola D'Aulaire

82   **Sports ears** means (has artificial ears, has a set he uses on special occasions, has unusual ears).

83   On land the tapir moves (clumsily, like an elephant, easily, stiffly).

84–85   In water the tapir moves (awkwardly, gracefully, solidly, quickly).

86–87   The tapir (has poor eyesight, has a limp, is not very clever, is deaf, walks badly).

88–90   Which parts of his body are said to be very strong? (His head, his tail, his neck, his eyes, his legs)

91   The tapir (doesn't like water, does like water, spends all his time in the water).

92   The tapir (is intelligent, thinks wisely, is not very intelligent).

Read the following carefully and then answer the questions. Where several possible answers are given, underline the correct answer.

If I were Lord of Tartary,
Myself, and me alone,
My bed should be of ivory,
Of beaten gold my throne;
And in my court should peacocks flaunt,
And in my forests tigers haunt,
And in my pools great fishes slant
Their fins athwart the sun.

From *Tartary* by Walter de la Mare

93 Ivory is: a kind of wood, a precious metal, <u>elephant tusks</u>, silver material

94-95 A peacock is: <u>a male bird</u>, a female bird, <u>a brightly coloured bird</u>, a grey bird

96 To flaunt is to: fly around, <u>strut about</u>, hide, shriek

97 "Beaten gold" is: the best quality gold, inferior gold, <u>gold that has been hammered into a particular shape</u>

98 Fins are used by a fish for: <u>swimming</u>, eating, sleeping

99 "Athwart" means: behind, under, <u>across</u>, above

100 Why does the speaker say "Myself and me alone"?: He is afraid of being alone, <u>he feels very important</u>, he is an only child

Paper 12

Read the following carefully, and then answer the questions.
Where several possible answers are given, underline the correct answer.

Cild Aelfric was physically very unlike his father. He was beardless, slight, weedy, and had a high somewhat girlish voice. His mouse-coloured hair hung lankly about his narrow ears. His stubby eyelashes were so light that one tended not to notice the cold shrewdness of the hazel eyes behind them. To the uninformed he appeared insignificant. Yet at nineteen he had won his honorary knightly title of "Cild" – "Childe" – by engineering a subtle plot for the massacre of four of his father's enemies. He possessed neither conscience nor fears. He paid lip-service to the observance of religion only when it suited him, and was entirely free from Alfhere's occasional attacks of worry over hell-fire and damnation.

(From *Avalon* by Anya Seton)

1–3   Cild Aelfric's father was (well-built, slim, beardless, manly, unlikeable, strong).

4   Cild Aelfric appeared to be (nondescript, important, charitable, popular, attractive).

5   **Subtle** means (slim, lithe, artful, generous).

6   **Paid lip-service to** means (talked a lot, was good at arguments, said he believed something but did not act as though he did, paid great attention to his appearance).

7   When you **engineer** something you (work machines, are scientific, contrive to bring something into being, work with your hands).

8–10   By Cild Aelfric's actions we know he was (clever, ruthless, noble, fearless, two-faced, brave).

Underline the word which has the same meaning as the word on the left.

11	**abandon**	ill-treat	forsake	unite	gather
12	**confer**	reveal	suggest	show	give
13	**suspect**	doubt	check	consider	feel
14	**robust**	round	fat	strong	tall
15	**integrate**	combine	roughen	separate	internal
16	**bulbous**	ugly	large	flower-like	like a bulb
17	**fatigued**	lazy	weary	slow	ill

59

In the following passage there are blanks. The jumbled word alongside each line should, when the letters are rearranged, make a word to fill the blank.

18 Last Saturday my friend and I went to a Dog Show.   **aaurstdy**

19 First we saw the Obedience Class.   **obcdeeein**

20 The dogs had to remain where they were, even   **narmei**

21 though their owners had walked away.   **swoner**

22 There were several other classes.   **verseal**

23 One was for toy dogs,   **oyt**

24 another one was for terriers   **trrreeis**

25 and a third was for hounds.   **hsunod**

26 The judges looked carefully at the   **jusdeg**

27 animals before awarding the   **slamina**

28 prizes . We had an enjoyable   **pzesir**

29 afternoon .   **annooetrf**

30-39 Make new words by adding the suffixes **ment** or **ship** to each of the following words. Write them in columns.

pay, member, hard, engage, state, friend, settle, scholar, arrange, owner

MENT	SHIP
pay	member
engage	hard
state	friend
settle	scholar
arrange	owner

Read the following carefully, and then answer the questions. Where several possible answers are given, underline the correct answer.

There is nothing like bad weather to reveal the shortcomings of a dwelling, particularly if it is too small. You are, as they say, stuck with it, and have leisure to feel all its peculiar irritations and discomforts. Bigwig, with his usual brisk energy, set to work. Hazel, however, returned and sat pensive at the lip of the hole, looking out at the silent, rippling veils of rain that drifted across and across the little valley between the two copses. Closer, before his nose, every blade of grass, every bracken frond was bent, dripping and glistening.

From *Watership Down* by Richard Adams

40–41 How does bad weather **reveal the shortcomings of a dwelling**? It shows (if it is too dark, if they are too crowded, if they don't have enough leisure, if it is too high, if it lets in the rain).

42 Hazel was (swinging, tired, thoughtful, cross, miserable).

43 The rain was (obscuring the view, making a loud noise, making Hazel very wet, running into the hole).

44 Why does the author say **across and across**? (To emphasise the fact that it didn't always go that way, because it happened repeatedly, because it was unusual)

45 The fronds were bent because (the rabbits had been running among them, the wind had knocked them down, the constant rain had pushed them over).

46 Which word in the passage means **gleaming**? glistening

47 Which word means **lively; active**? brisk

Complete the following expressions by putting the correct number in each space.

48	slow and	(3)	(1)	**span**
49	fast and	(7)	(2)	**rave**
50	safe and	(5)	(3)	**sure**
51	spick and	(1)	(4)	**ready**
52	body and	(9)	(5)	**sound**
53	touch and	(8)	(6)	**foot**
54	hand and	(6)	(7)	**furious**
55	rant and	(2)	(8)	**go**
56	rough and	(4)	(9)	**soul**

57-66 Here are the words which are missing from the extract below. Can you put them in the right places?

**movement   wedge   cook   ashore   crutch   deck   walk   spaces
lanyard   heaviest**

Long John Silver, our ship's ___cook___ – Barbecue as the men called him – carried his ___crutch___ by a ___lanyard___ round his neck, to have both hands as free as possible. It was something to see him ___wedge___ the foot of his crutch against a bulkhead, and, propped against it, yielding to every ___movement___ of the ship, get on with his cooking like someone safe ___ashore___. Still more strange was it to see him in the ___heaviest___ of weather, cross the ___deck___. He had a line or two rigged up to help him across the widest ___spaces___ and he would hand himself from one place to another as quickly as another man could ___walk___.

From *Treasure Island* by R. L. Stevenson

Write the opposites of the following words:

67	contract	expand	68 import	export
69	increase	decrease	70 fine	coarse
71	captive	free	72 temporary	permanent
73	superior	inferior	74 refuse	accept
75	plural	singular	76 adult	child

Match the people and animals in the column on the left with their homes on the right.

77	lion	(3)	(1) **hutch**
78	spider	(5)	(2) **eyrie**
79	squirrel	(8)	(3) **den**
80	nun	(7)	(4) **barracks**
81	bee	(10)	(5) **web**
82	rabbit	(1)	(6) **caravan**
83	mouse	(11)	(7) **convent**
84	bird	(9)	(8) **drey**

85 eagle ...(2)... (9) **nest**

86 gipsy ...(6)... (10) **hive**

87 soldier ...(4)... (11) **hole**

Underline the word on each line which has the same meaning as the word on the left, and ring the word which has an opposite meaning.

88–89 **blame** wrong careless censure bad ⟨praise⟩

90–91 **elevate** high raise ⟨lower⟩ elude bottom

92–93 **assemble** ⟨disperse⟩ asunder together unite gather

94–95 **expand** larger ⟨contract⟩ smaller increase disband

Write the masculine forms of the following words:

96 daughter-in-law son-in-law   97 her   him

98 heiress   heir   99 madam   sir

100 stewardess   steward

Date

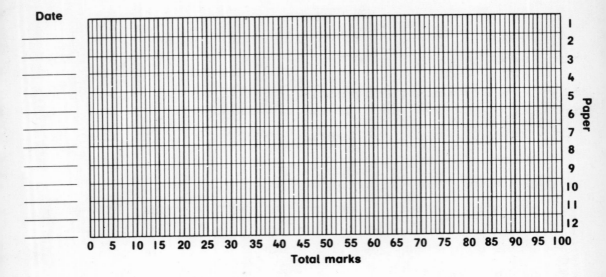

Total marks

Thomas Nelson and Sons Ltd
Nelson House Mayfield Road
Walton-on-Thames Surrey
KT12 5PL UK

© **J M Bond** 1988, 1994

First published 1988
This fully revised edition 1994

I(T)P Thomas Nelson is an International
       Thomson Publishing Company

I(T)P is used under licence

Pupil's book   ISBN 0-17-424529-7
                NPN 9 8 7 6
Answer book ISBN 0-17-424530-0
                NPN 9 8 7 6

By the same author
First, Second, Third, Fourth and Further Fourth Year
Assessment Papers in Mathematics

First, Second, Third, Fourth and Further
Fourth Year Assessment Papers in English

First, Second, Third and Fourth and Further
Fourth Year Assessment Papers in Reasoning

Printed in Croatia.

Poems and extracts reproduced by kind permission of

Allen & Unwin for 'All Day it has Rained' by Alun Lewis (Paper
1) and *The Hobbit* by J R R Tolkien (Paper 8);
The Bodley Head for *Silver on the Tree* by S Cooper (Paper 2);
Century Hutchinson for 'Family Holiday' by Raymond Wilson
(Paper 4);
Rex Collings for *Watership Down* by Richard Adams (Paper 6
and Paper 12);
Collins Publishers for *My Family and Other Animals* by
Gerald Durrell (Paper 3);
Geffrey Dearmer for 'The Giraffe' (Paper 9);
Encyclopaedia Britannica for 'Bees', adapted from
'Hymenoptera' in *Encyclopaedia Britannica* (15th Edition)
1974 9:129 (Paper 4);
Faber & Faber Ltd for 'Empty House' by Stephen Spender
(Paper 5);
Hodder & Stoughton for *Avalon* by Anya Seton (Paper 12);
Hogarth Press for *Cider with Rosie* by Laurie Lee (Paper 8);
Hughes Massie Ltd for *Jennie* by Paul Gallico (Paper 5);
Muller Blond & White Ltd for 'Pigeons' by Richard Kell
(Paper 5) and 'Spraying Sheep' by Norman MacCaig (Paper 10);
Oxford University Press for *Warrior Scarlet* by
Rosemary Sutcliffe (Paper 3);
Schofield & Sims for 'At The Theatre' by A P Herbert
(Paper 11).
The Literary Trustees of Walter de la Mare and the Society of
Authors as their representative for 'Tartary' by Walter de la
Mare (Paper 11)

The publishers have made every attempt to trace copyright
holders of reprinted material, and apologise for any errors or
omissions.